QUIZ WHIZ

QUIZ PACK 3

Play With Your Food

WHAT'S THE PROBLEM? I'M TOTALLY A FUN-GI!

Eat My Words!

1. **Roald Dahl wrote a book about a boy and a giant piece of which fruit?**
   a. peach
   b. plum
   c. pineapple
   d. pear

2. ***Bunnicula* is a story about a bunny that does what?**
   a. turns into a bat
   b. bites vegetables and drains them of their juices
   c. grows garlic to fight vampires
   d. lives on a farm in Transylvania

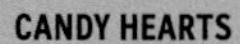

CANDY HEARTS

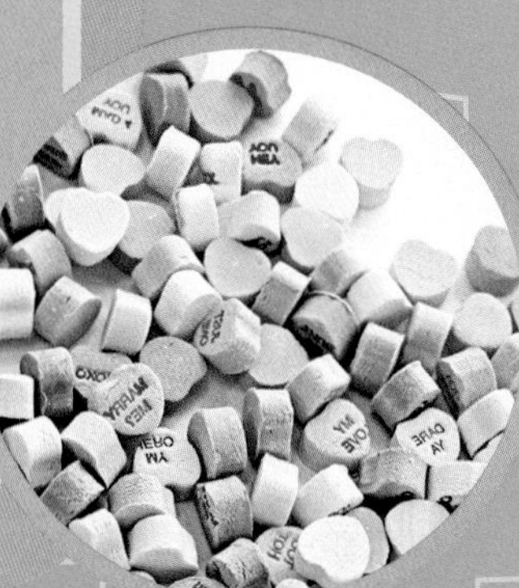

3. **In the nursery rhyme "Little Jack Horner," what was Jack eating?**
   a. Christmas pie
   b. Thanksgiving turkey
   c. candy hearts
   d. chocolate eggs

4. **In what folktale does a hungry stranger trick a villager into helping him make a delicious meal?**
   a. "Yummy Casserole"
   b. "Stone Soup"
   c. "Tricky Pizza"
   d. "Delish Dish"

5. **Shel Silverstein's poem "Hungry Mungry" is about a boy who eats which of the following?**
   a. a shank of lamb
   b. four chocolate shakes
   c. the universe
   d. all of the above

6. **True or false?** The strange food weather in the book *Cloudy With a Chance of Meatballs* takes place in the village of YumYumville.

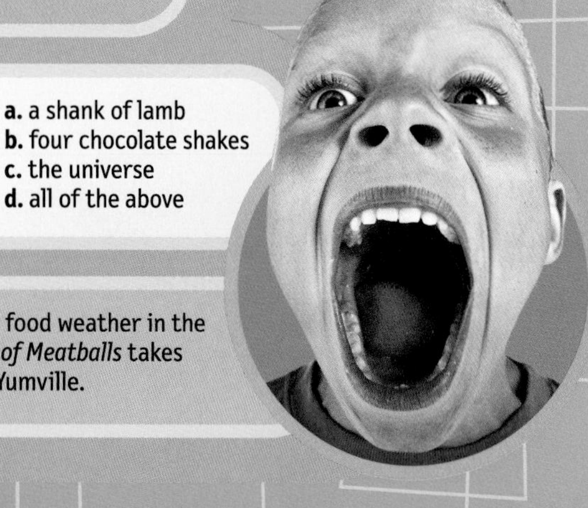

7 **True or false?** In the movie *Ratatouille*, Remy the rat creates a delicious vegetable stew.

8 **Which is the name of a book by Judy Bloom about a boy who makes a disgusting drink in order to get freckles?**

a. *Freckle Shake*
b. *Freckle Potion*
c. *Freckle Fountain*
d. *Freckle Juice*

9 **Hans Christian Andersen wrote a famous fairy tale about a girl who can feel which food under her mattress?**

a. a soybean
b. a banana
c. a pork chop
d. a pea

10 **In the song "On Top of Spaghetti," what was lost when somebody sneezed?**

a. noodles
b. marshmallows
c. a meatball
d. a sense of humor

11 **True or false?** In the book *The Chronicles of Narnia: The Lion, the Witch and the Wardrobe*, the White Witch gives Edmund a slice of coconut cake at their first meeting.

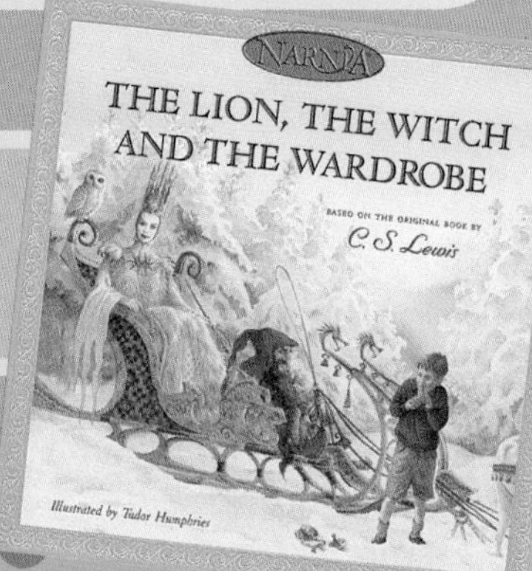

CHECK YOUR ANSWERS ON PAGES 22–23.

Mind Your Manners

1 In Chile, which is the preferred method for eating french fries?

a. eating them with a knife and fork
b. eating them from a paper cone
c. eating them with lots of ketchup
d. eating them inside sandwiches and burgers

2 In traditional Korean dining, where would guests sit?

a. on the floor
b. at a round table
c. on the sidewalk
d. outdoors

3 True or false? In Japan, it is considered rude to stand your chopsticks up in your rice bowl.

4 The Continental style of dining favored by Europeans means what?

a. Plates are in the different shapes of continents.
b. A fork is held in your left hand and a knife in your right.
c. All meals are eaten outdoors.
d. Dining guests are expected to name all continents before getting dessert.

5 What does the book *Emily Post's Table Manners for Kids* advise about texting when dining?

a. It is perfectly acceptable.
b. It is acceptable if the host is also texting.
c. It is acceptable to text once dessert is served.
d. It is never acceptable to text during a meal.

6 What do Bedouins in the Middle East do to signal that they do not want more coffee?

a. put a chair on the table
b. shake a cup
c. shout, "Enough!"
d. wink three times

7 Which food did early Greeks give guests as a symbol of hospitality?

a. olives
b. bananas
c. Greek salad
d. salt

8 If a German host calls out "Guten Appetit!" before you eat, what is the host saying to you?

a. "May your gut be filled with good food."
b. "German food is yummy."
c. "Enjoy your meal!"
d. "Rub-a-dub-dub, here comes the grub!"

9 True or false? Loudly slurping soup in Japan is an offense that carries a hefty fine.

10 Which custom is common to many parts of Asia, Africa, and the Middle East but not to Europe and the United States?

a. singing at the table
b. eating with your hands
c. not speaking at the table
d. eating dessert first

11 In South India, you should never touch your plate with what?

a. your fork
b. your neighbor's elbow
c. a shoe
d. your left hand

CHECK YOUR ANSWERS ON PAGES 22–23.

Snacks From the Sea

1 True or false? The amount of wild fish and shellfish caught from the ocean each year is about three times the total weight of every person in the United States.

2 What is the name of a tasty fish found in southeast Asia that can move short distances over land?

a. U-Haul fish
b. lungfish
c. walking catfish
d. blue jumper

3 What is another name for the Chilean sea bass, a popular fish served in many seafood restaurants?

a. Patagonian toothfish
b. slippery codswallop
c. joker fish
d. SpongeBob BigBass

4 A cousin to the grouper that is also popular for dinner is called ______ in South Carolina, U.S.A.

a. cousin flipper
b. wreckfish
c. Sam
d. blue whale

5 True or false? Roughly half of all seafood is raised and farmed by humans.

6 How is the tambaqui different from its flesh-eating cousin, the piranha?

a. It only eats the flesh of hippos.
b. It is vegetarian.
c. It has legs.
d. It has twice as many teeth.

7 Black squid ink is a popular ingredient in some pasta dishes. Why do squid squirt ink?

a. to confuse predators
b. to attract a mate
c. to use in letter writing
d. to show off

8 What live seafood can be bought at a vending machine in China?

a. octopus
b. sardines
c. slithering eels
d. hairy crabs

9 True or false? A bluefin tuna weighing 754 pounds (342 kg) sold at auction in Tokyo for $420,000.

10 On *The Simpsons* television show, what was the name of Homer Simpson's pet lobster?

a. Claws
b. Sir Grab-A-Lot
c. Pinchy
d. Bart

CHECK YOUR ANSWERS ON PAGES 22–23.

MAP MANIA!

Global Grub

1 TURKEY

True or false? The shish kebab may have originated with medieval Turkish soldiers who used their swords to grill meat over open fires.

NORTH AMERICA

ATLANTIC OCEAN

PACIFIC OCEAN

SOUTH AMERICA

E

C

2 ICELAND

In addition to smoking salmon, some people in Iceland catch this fish and let it rot before eating it.

a. halibut
b. catfish
c. goldfish
d. shark

3 MEXICO

On the Day of the Dead in Mexico, people bake a sweet bread called *pan de muerto*. What does *pan de muerto* mean?

a. bone bread
b. snacker crackers
c. bread of the dead
d. pan of skeleton

How much do you know about grub around the globe? Test your knowledge of food traditions from many cultures and then match each yummy treat to the country where it came from on the map.

4 GERMANY

Which surprising ingredient can often be found in Germany's traditional cookie *pfeffernüsse*? Hint: You might find it near the salt.

a. eye of newt
b. pepper
c. mango
d. candy canes

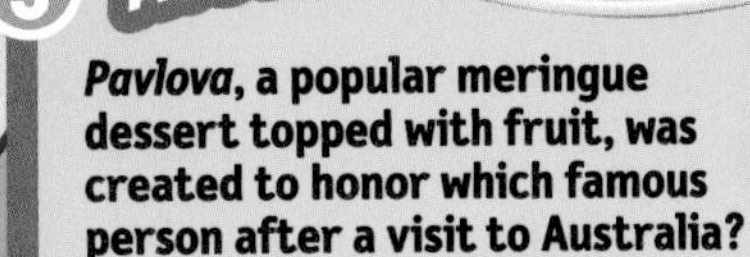

5 AUSTRALIA

***Pavlova*, a popular meringue dessert topped with fruit, was created to honor which famous person after a visit to Australia?**

a. Russian ballerina Anna Pavlova
b. Jamaican bobsled champion Deon Pavlova
c. British teen pop star Pavlova Spears
d. Polish president Pyotr Pavlova

6 SOUTH AFRICA

True or false? Bunny chow is a traditional South African dish of curried rabbit served in a bread bowl.

7–12 ORANGE MARKERS

SHOW WHERE EACH OF THESE TASTY MORSELS CAN BE FOUND. MATCH EACH FOOD TO ITS COUNTRY OF ORIGIN ON THE MAP.

CHECK YOUR ANSWERS ON PAGES 22–23.

TRUE or FALSE?

Extreme Eats

1. A 1,000-POUND (453-KG) BUTTER SCULPTURE ON DISPLAY AT A FAIR WAS LATER USED TO PROVIDE ELECTRICITY ON A FARM FOR THREE DAYS.
2. THE LATIN NAME FOR COCOA IS *THEOBROMA*, WHICH LITERALLY MEANS "SWEET DARKNESS."
3. MORE THAN 700 PEOPLE IN DALLAS, TEXAS, U.S.A., DRESSED AS CLOWNS AND HAD A CREAM PIE FIGHT TO RAISE MONEY FOR CHARITIES.
4. DURIAN FRUIT IS SO SMELLY IT IS NOT ALLOWED ON PUBLIC TRANSPORTATION IN SOUTHEAST ASIA.
5. A WOMAN IN SUSSEX, ENGLAND, U.K., ATE 7,175 PEAS IN 60 MINUTES.
6. MORE THAN 40,000 PEOPLE POUR INTO THE STREETS AND HURL CHEESE AT EACH OTHER DURING SPAIN'S LA TOMATINA FESTIVAL.
7. THE WORLD RECORD FOR THE NUMBER OF EARTHWORMS EATEN IN 30 SECONDS IS 59.
8. IN INDONESIA, SNAKE MEAT IS CONSIDERED TABOO AND IS NEVER EATEN.
9. EDIBLE LEAFCUTTER ANTS ARE BEING PROMOTED AS A HIGH-PROTEIN ALTERNATIVE TO BEEF AND PORK.
10. A GROUP CALLED "CANSTRUCTION" SPONSORS DESIGN COMPETITIONS WHERE PARTICIPANTS BUILD STRUCTURES MADE ENTIRELY OF CANNED GOODS.
11. THE WINNER OF AN EATING CONTEST IN CALIFORNIA, U.S.A., ATE 55 DUMPLINGS IN 10 MINUTES.
12. AN ITALIAN CHEESE MADE OF SHEEP'S MILK IS SOFTENED THROUGH THE INTRODUCTION OF MAGGOTS.
13. THE UNITED KINGDOM'S HELEN JUCKES HOLDS THE RECORD FOR THE FASTEST MARATHON TIME FOR A FEMALE DRESSED AS A STALK OF BROCCOLI.
14. THE WORLD'S LARGEST PIZZA DELIVERY HAPPENED WITH 30,000 PIZZAS SENT FROM ILLINOIS, U.S.A., TO THE ARMED FORCES IN AFGHANISTAN.
15. A POTATO CHIP FLAVORED LIKE ROAST OX CAN BE FOUND IN PERU.

16 THE POMELO IS A CITRUS FRUIT OFTEN GIVEN AS A GIFT DURING MEXICO'S DAY OF THE DEAD CELEBRATION.

17 THE DANDELION, CONSIDERED A WEED BY GARDENERS, IS ALSO EATEN AS A SALAD GREEN.

18 A QUAHOG IS ANOTHER NAME FOR A CUPCAKE.

19 IN FINLAND, YOU CAN DINE IN A CAVE RESTAURANT 262 FEET (80 M) UNDERGROUND.

20 YOU CAN BE SERVED BY ROBOTS IN A HONG KONG RESTAURANT CALLED ROBOT KITCHEN.

21 YOU CANNOT SQUEEZE JUICE FROM A CACTUS.

22 A SAN FRANCISCO ENGINEER HAS CREATED A LIQUID THAT HE CLAIMS WILL REPLACE FOOD IN THE FUTURE.

23 A TYPE OF CHILI PEPPER GROWN IN INDIA IS THREE THOUSAND TO FOUR THOUSAND TIMES HOTTER THAN A JALAPEÑO.

24 VULTURES CAN DINE ON TASTY ROADKILL AT A SPECIAL VULTURE RESTAURANT IN TURKEY.

25 STRAW IS THE PRIMARY INGREDIENT IN THE CHINESE DELICACY BIRD'S NEST SOUP.

26 IN SWEDEN, BEEF TONGUE ICE CREAM IS A POPULAR FLAVOR.

27 IN 1919, A TANK FILLED WITH MORE THAN 2 MILLION GALLONS (7.5 MILLION L) OF MOLASSES EXPLODED AND FLOODED STREETS IN BOSTON, MASSACHUSETTS, U.S.A.

28 TO MAKE MILK LOOK FRESHLY POURED IN ADVERTISEMENTS, PUDDING IS ADDED TO MAKE FROTHY BUBBLES.

29 A BRITISH CANDY MAKER MADE A GOLD-COVERED CHOCOLATE CANDY BAR.

30 IN A RESTAURANT IN SYDNEY, AUSTRALIA, YOU CAN ORDER A ROO PIZZA THAT INCLUDES STRIPS OF MARINATED CROCODILE.

CHECK YOUR ANSWERS ON PAGES 22–23.

Grow Your Groceries

1 **How many pounds of tomatoes does the average American eat each year?**

a. 2 pounds (.9 kg)
b. 22 pounds (10 kg)
c. 40 pounds (18 kg)
d. 180 pounds (82 kg)

2 **True or false?** Raspberries and blueberries have long been used as dyes to color cotton and wool.

3 **About how many squirts of milk from a cow does it take to make a gallon of milk?**

a. 15
b. 79
c. 150
d. 350

4 **How many honeybees does it take to make one tablespoon of honey?**

a. 1
b. 12
c. 50
d. 1,500

5 **How many gallons of water are needed to produce one bushel of corn?**

a. 12
b. 50
c. 500
d. 4,000

6 **A Roman emperor's son loved which vegetable so much that he refused to eat anything else for an entire month?**

a. broccoli
b. string beans
c. carrots
d. beets

7 **Eggplants are related to which food?**

a. beets
b. tomatoes
c. potatoes
d. plums

8 **Which U.S. state grows the most grapes?**

a. Montana
b. Florida
c. California
d. Hawaii

9 **Which of the following has been used to treat headaches, toothaches, animal bites, and the plague?**

a. yams
b. applesauce
c. garlic
d. spinach

10 **Which food is believed to be the first crop grown for food?**

a. apples
b. figs
c. broccoli
d. popcorn

11 **True or false?** Squash got its name from a cooking method in which the gourd was squashed before baking.

12 **The strawberry is a member of which plant family?**

a. cherry
b. rose
c. pumpkin
d. Venus flytrap

CHECK YOUR ANSWERS ON PAGES 22–23.

Street Food

KOSHARI

1 **Egypt's national dish, *koshari*, is a spicy stew filled with rice, lentils, garlic, and chickpeas and topped with what?**

a. raw eggs
b. crispy fried onions
c. glitter
d. lemon peel

2 **Where are you most likely to find street vendors selling barbecued stingrays?**

a. at a very weird water park
b. Denmark
c. Malaysia
d. the lost food court of Atlantis

BARBECUED STINGRAY

3 **What is the name of a common fried dough treat found at amusement parks in the United States?**

a. puffed sugar pies
b. fry puppies
c. fun dough
d. funnel cake

4 **Which of the following rodents is a popular grilled food in Peru?**

a. mole rat
b. guinea pig
c. porcupine
d. gerbil

5 **Which skewered treat is sold in the Philippines?**

a. chicken intestines
b. earthworms
c. candied string beans
d. barbecued beef jerky

6 **What hearty lunch soup can you buy from vendors in Shanghai?**

a. alphabet soup with carrots
b. ostrich and onions
c. split pea with artichoke
d. duck blood and glass noodle

7 **Which of these foods is a common sweet treat in Malaysia?**

a. jackfruit
b. alligator snouts
c. goose in cherry soup
d. lemon puffs

8 **True or false?** Deep-fried spiders are a crunchy snack sold in Cambodia.

TARANTULA

9 **What chocolate-covered treat was served at a street festival in New York? Hint: It was also green.**

a. pickle
b. fish eye
c. Italian sausage
d. frog leg

10 **True or false?** Some food trucks in Alaska, U.S.A., sell reindeer hot dogs.

11 **A bouquet of grasshoppers in China's street food scene provides a healthy boost of what?**

a. vitamin C
b. protein
c. sugar
d. carbohydrates

GRASSHOPPERS

CHECK YOUR ANSWERS ON PAGES 22–23.

Sweet Treats

1 The world's first desserts were probably eaten in ____.

a. U.S.A.
b. India
c. France
d. Russia

2 True or false? Bees in France began producing blue and green honey when they fed on waste from a nearby M&M candy factory.

3 Which of the following is *not* a Bertie Bott's jellybean flavor from the *Harry Potter* series?

a. centipede
b. paper
c. toenails
d. whistle spit

4 At Greek weddings it is customary to serve an odd number of pieces of this candy to wedding guests.

a. Easter eggs
b. candy canes
c. candy-coated almonds
d. Hershey's kisses

5 According to ice-cream maker Baskin-Robbins, if you like chocolate chip ice cream, you are probably a ____ person.

a. cautious
b. confident
c. generous
d. dramatic

6 Cotton candy made its debut at the 1904 World's Fair. What was its original name?

a. sticky stucco
b. fairy floss
c. pink tornado
d. spun fun

7 True or false? The owners of Krispy Kreme doughnuts cut a hole in the side of their bakery so they could sell to people on the sidewalk.

8 How much water does it take to make one pound (.5 kg) of dark chocolate?

a. 1 gallon (4 L)
b. 27 gallons (102 L)
c. 542 gallons (2,052 L)
d. 3,170 gallons (12,000 L)

9 True or false? White chocolate does not contain any chocolate.

10 One British candy maker claims to have made a chocolate bar that doesn't do what?

a. melt
b. taste good
c. look like chocolate
d. hold a shape

11 Which ingredient is not included in traditional fudge?

a. butter
b. chocolate
c. sugar
d. milk

CHECK YOUR ANSWERS ON PAGES 22–23.

GAME SHOW

ULTIMATE FOOD CHALLENGE

1 **When bees visit flowers, what do they eat and later turn into honey?**

a. nectar
b. leaf
c. stem
d. root

2 **In which state could you find a giant statue of a buttered, baked potato in front of a museum?**

a. Rhode Island
b. Idaho
c. Florida
d. Hawaii

3 **What does the video game character Pac-Man eat?**

a. candy corn
b. barbecued bananas
c. mushroom magnets
d. power pellets

4 **Which type of restaurant is most associated with Brazil?**

a. sushi bar
b. pizza place
c. noodle shop
d. steak house

5 **NASA astronaut Don Pettit wrote about growing vegetables on the International Space Station. What was the name of his blog?**

a. Broccoli Rocket
b. Mean Green Space Beans
c. Diary of a Space Zucchini
d. Try to Beet Me to Mars

6 **A hawk that eats a frog that eats a grasshopper that eats grass is an example of what?**

a. bad manners
b. food chain
c. ecosystem
d. nature gone wild

7 **TRUE OR FALSE?**

A long time ago, people would expose fruits and vegetables to the sun and wind in order to preserve them.

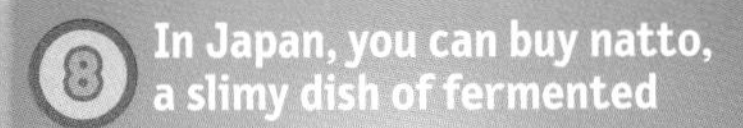

8 In Japan, you can buy natto, a slimy dish of fermented ________.

a. horsehair
b. soybeans
c. eel
d. asparagus

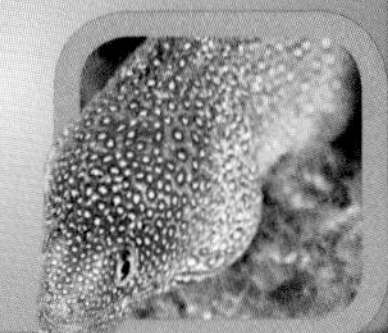

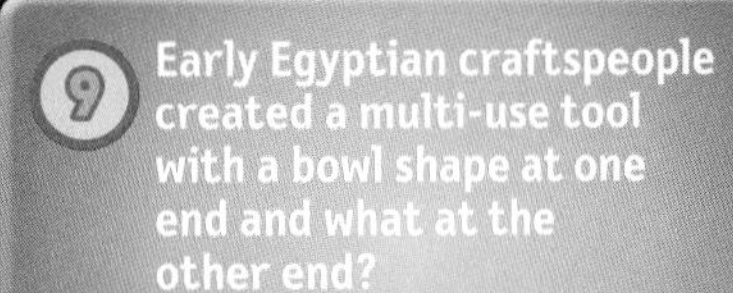

9 Early Egyptian craftspeople created a multi-use tool with a bowl shape at one end and what at the other end?

a. a hook to extract snails from their shells
b. a fork with six tines
c. scissors for cutting hair
d. a sword

10 TRUE OR FALSE?

The Central Andean Indians in Peru were not successful at growing crops at high elevations.

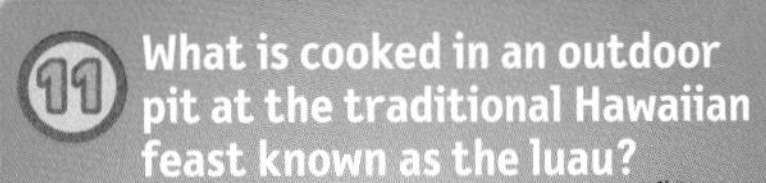

11 What is cooked in an outdoor pit at the traditional Hawaiian feast known as the luau?

a. pig
b. fish
c. spinach
d. pumpkin soup

12 ________ was so important to the medieval diet, there were laws about baking and selling it.

a. bread
b. cabbage
c. meat
d. pizza

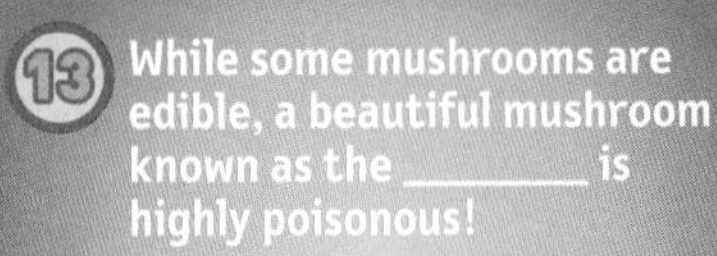

13 While some mushrooms are edible, a beautiful mushroom known as the ________ is highly poisonous!

a. skull and crossbones
b. death cap
c. mush of death
d. goner 'shroom

14 TRUE OR FALSE?

A key ingredient in shoofly pie is a common housefly.

15 ULTIMATE BRAIN BUSTER

SHAVING CREAM, GLUE, AND EXPLOSIVES ARE JUST A FEW OF THE PRODUCTS MADE FROM WHICH FOOD?

a. 
eggs

b. 
carrots

c. 
peanuts

d. 
ice pops

CHECK YOUR ANSWERS ON PAGES 22–23.

ANSWERS

Eat My Words! pages 4–5

1. a
2. b
3. a
4. b
5. d
6. **False.** The classic tale by Judi Barrett takes place in a tiny town called Chewandswallow.
7. **True.** The French stew ratatouille is usually made with tomatoes, garlic, onions, zucchini, eggplant, peppers, and a mixture of tasty herbs.
8. d
9. d
10. c
11. **False.** She gives Edmund his favorite food, a sweet treat known as Turkish Delight.

Mind Your Manners, pages 6–7

1. a
2. a
3. **True.** It resembles incense burning, symbolizing offering food for the dead.
4. b
5. d
6. b
7. d
8. c
9. **False.** Slurping is considered an acceptable and enjoyable way to eat soup in Japan.
10. b
11. d

Snacks From the Sea, pages 8–9

1. **True.** More than 170 billion pounds (77.9 million metric tons) of seafood are caught each year.
2. c
3. a
4. b
5. **True.** Shrimp, salmon, and oysters are some of the seafood that is farmed.
6. b
7. a
8. d
9. **True.** It was bought jointly by owners of a restaurant in Hong Kong and a chain of sushi bars.
10. c

Map Mania! Global Grub, pages 10–11

1. **True.** In Greece, a similar skewered food is prepared called souvlaki.
2. d
3. c
4. b
5. a
6. **False.** There is no rabbit in bunny chow. Originally these spicy bread bowls were vegetarian, but later versions added mutton, lamb, or chicken.
7. Turkey, **D**
8. Iceland, **C**
9. Mexico, **E**
10. Germany, **B**
11. Australia, **F**
12. South Africa, **A**

Extreme Eats, pages 12–13

1. **True.** The sculpture was dumped into a special pit that turns waste into energy.
2. **False.** *Theobroma's* literal translation is "food of the gods."
3. **True.** In order not to be wasteful of food, the "cream" pies were actually shaving cream!
4. **True.** The fruit is pungent, with some people saying it smells like dirty socks and bad cheese.
5. **True.** Janet Harris ate each of the 7,175 peas one by one using chopsticks!
6. **False.** People throw tomatoes. The tomatoes have to be crushed first to avoid injuries.
7. **False.** In 2003, a man in India swallowed 200 earthworms measuring at least 4 inches (10 cm) in 30 seconds.
8. **False.** In addition to burgers, snake meat is used in soups, shish kebabs, and even beverages.
9. **True.** Hoping to put an end to worldwide famine, the United Nations is actively promoting edible insects as a sustainable food source.
10. **True.** Canstruction's goal is to bring awareness to hunger issues around the world. The canned food is donated to local food banks.
11. **False.** Joey "Jaws" Chestnut actually ate a record 266 dumplings!
12. **True.** If you are squeamish about eating live maggots, you can put the cheese in a sealed bag until they die.
13. **False.** Juckes completed the race in 3 hours 47 minutes 15 seconds dressed as a carrot.
14. **True.** The 12-inch pizzas were made by Great Kitchens and delivered on July 4, 2012, just in time for Independence Day.
15. **False.** Roast Ox–flavored potato chips can be found in England.
16. **False.** The pomelo is a gift given during Chinese New Year's and is a symbol of prosperity and good luck.
17. **True.** The dandelion is used in fresh salads or sometimes sautéed in oil. It's packed with Vitamin K.
18. **False.** A quahog is a hard-shelled clam found in the waters off Cape Cod in the United States.
19. **True.** The restaurant is located in an abandoned limestone mine.
20. **True.** Robots take orders, deliver meals, prepare omelets, and even flip burgers!
21. **False.** Juice from the prickly pear cactus is filled with nutrients.
22. **True.** The inventor of Soylent claims that the liquid has all the nutrition that humans need to live.
23. **True.** India's Naga king chili is the hottest known pepper in the world.
24. **True.** Part of a conservation area for birds, the vulture restaurant is a drop-off site for roadkill, butcher shop remains, and the carcasses of dead farm animals.
25. **False.** Bird saliva is the primary ingredient in the soup that has been prized in China for its health benefits for more than 1,000 years.
26. **False.** Beef-tongue ice cream is popular in Japan. Other unusual flavors include eel, raw horse, curry, crab, and octopus!
27. **True.** The sticky flood pushed buildings off their foundations and killed 21 people.
28. **False.** Food photographers use dish soap and many other unappetizing tricks to make food look tasty for the camera.
29. **True.** The gilded sweet was auctioned off at $1,600, and the money was donated to charity.
30. **False.** The *roo* is actually kangaroo, and it's the most popular pizza on the menu.

Grow Your Groceries, pages 14–15

1. b
2. **True.** Cultures around the world have used natural dyes to add color to their clothing and household items and even to decorate their bodies!
3. d
4. b
5. d
6. a
7. c
8. c

. c
. b
1. **False.** It comes from the Narragansett Native American word *askutasquash*, which means "eaten raw."
2. **b**

Street Food, pages 16–17

1. **b**
2. **c**
3. **d**
4. **b**
5. **a**
6. **d**
7. **a**
8. **True.** Tarantulas are considered a local delicacy and are sometimes enjoyed sprinkled with soy sauce.
9. **a**
10. **True.** Head to downtown Anchorage to sample Alaska's best reindeer dogs with all the toppings. Just don't tell Santa!
11. **b**

Sweet Treats, pages 18–19

1. **b**
2. **True.** Beekeepers were stumped by the colorful honey until their investigation found the bees feasting on the colored candy shells.
3. **d**
4. **c**
5. **c**
6. **b**
7. **True.** The smells from the Krispy Kreme bakery in Winston-Salem, North Carolina, U.S.A., were so delicious to neighbors they wanted to buy right from the sidewalk.
8. **d**
9. **True.** White chocolate is made from cocoa butter, sugar, and vanilla and is actually not chocolate.
10. **a**
11. **b**

Game Show: Ultimate Food Challenge, pages 20–21

1. **a**
2. **b**
3. **d**
4. **d**
5. **c**
6. **b**
7. **True.** Removing moisture dries out the food and slows the rate at which it spoils.
8. **b**
9. **a**
10. **False.** They were extremely successful, developing techniques of finding vegetables and grain that thrived at high altitudes and creating stone terraces to increase the amount of flat land for crops.
11. **a**
12. **a**
13. **b**
14. **False.** This delicious pie found in the region of the United States called Pennsylvania Dutch Country has sweet molasses in it, but no flies!
15. **a**

SCORING

0–40

FOOD FOR THOUGHT

Food facts are probably not your idea of fabulous fun, but some of life's most delicious discoveries are found on our plates. We learn a lot about our world and ourselves by understanding more about what we eat. Open your mind and mouth to the food around you.

41–81

SOMETHING TO CHEW ON

Your food knowledge is a buffet of facts and insights. You take a bite out of life and savor the world around you. Keep feeding yourself facts and digesting the information to become a true expert on all things edible.

82–123

A BANQUET OF KNOWLEDGE

When it comes to tasty trivia, you feast like royalty. Whether it's fried, boiled, pickled, or baked, you've got the dish on food. Keep drinking in the food facts around you, and, who knows, one day they may even name a dessert after you. Sweet!

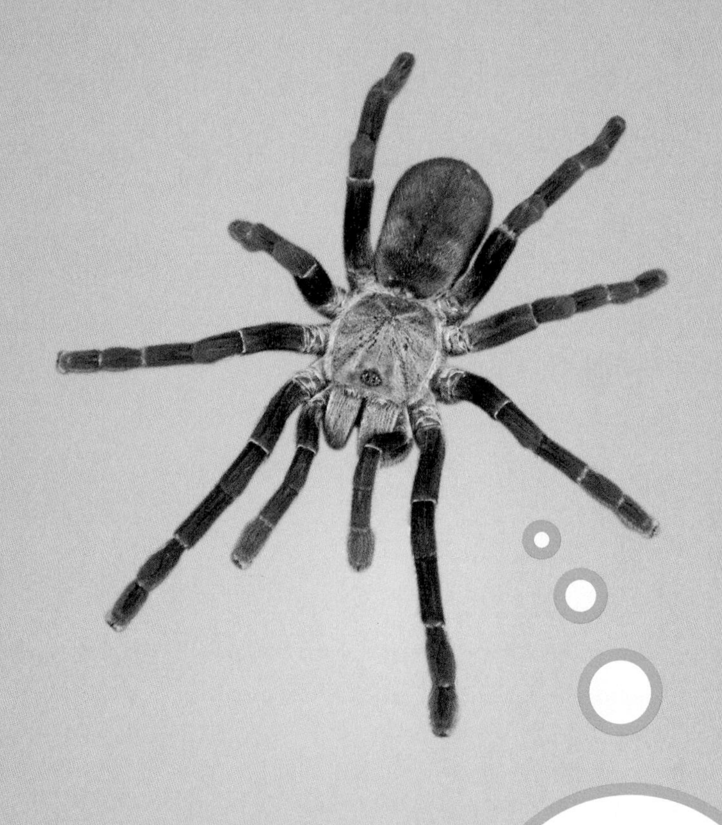

NOW YOU'RE
A QUIZ WHIZ!

15/KG/3